Game of Stones

by Rebecca Lisle

illustrated by
Richard Watson

For Tyrese. R.L.
For

The Stone Age was boring.

"I'm *so* bored," said Pod's little brother, Hinge.
"What can we do?"
"I'll invent a new game," Pod said. "Just for you!"

"Here you are!" Pod said. "This is whizzy!"

"Wow! Fantastic!" Hinge cried.

"What shall we call it?"

"I'll call it a Yow-Yow," Pod said.
"That Yow-Yow is banned!" Dad said.

"Never mind little Hinge," said Pod.
"I'll make you something even better."

Pod chiselled and sawed...

...and hammered...

...and made these:

"In this game you try and hit the ball before I knock the bones down."

"Oh, oh, careful Hinge! Not so hard Hinge!"

"Sorry!" Pod said. "I'll call that game Crackit."
"Well Crackit's banned too," Dad said.

"But it was fun," said Hinge.
"Go and play somewhere else!" Mum said.

Pod thought and thought.

He had some brilliant ideas...

...but Hinge didn't like any of them.

What would be a perfect toy for little Hinge?

"I have a great idea!" Pod thought.

Pod chiselled and cut...

...and sanded and scraped.

We need somewhere away from Mum and Dad!"

"Where?" Hinge asked.
"Ah ha!" Pod cried, "I have had another huge idea!"

The woolly mammoths helped.

The birds and lizards helped. Pod's friends helped.

"Wow! That's cool! A play park!"
"I've thought of a great name for it too..." Pod said.

Game of Stones

is an original concept by
© 2017 Rebecca Lisle

Author: Rebecca Lisle
Illustrator: Richard Watson

A CIP catalogue record for this book is available at the British Library.

Published by MAVERICK ARTS PUBLISHING LTD

Studio 3A, City Business Centre, 6 Brighton Road,
Horsham, West Sussex, RH13 5BB
© Maverick Arts Publishing Limited November 2017
+44 (0)1403 256941

ISBN 978-1-84886-299-9

I wonder what it was used for?

www.maverickbooks.co.uk